FORBIDDEN CLASSROOM

BATTLE IN THE STARS

Written by Tony Bradman

Illustrated by Dylan Gibson

RISING STARS

ISBN: 9781398324251

Text © 2022 Tony Bradman
Illustrations, design and layout © Hodder and Stoughton Ltd
First published in 2022 by Hodder & Stoughton Limited (for its Rising Stars imprint, part of the Hodder Education Group),
An Hachette UK Company
Carmelite House, 50 Victoria Embankment, London EC4Y 0DZ

www.risingstars-uk.com

Impression number 10 9 8 7 6 5 4 3 2 1
Year 2026 2025 2024 2023 2022

Author: Tony Bradman
Series Editor: Tony Bradman
Commissioning Editor: Hamish Baxter
Educational Reviewer: Helen Marron
Illustrator: Dylan Gibson
Design: Helen Townson
Page layout: Stephanie White/Kamae Design Ltd
Editor: Amy Tyrer

With thanks to the schools that took part in the development of Reading Planet KS2, including: Ancaster CE Primary School, Ancaster; Downsway Primary School, Reading; Ferry Lane Primary School, London; Foxborough Primary School, Slough; Griffin Park Primary School, Blackburn; St Barnabas CE First & Middle School, Pershore; Tranmoor Primary School, Doncaster; and Wilton CE Primary School, Wilton.

A catalogue record for this title is available from the British Library.

Printed in India.

Orders: Please contact Hachette UK Distribution, Hely Hutchinson Centre, Milton Road, Didcot, Oxfordshire, OX11 7HH.
Telephone: (44) 01235 400555. Email: primary@hachette.co.uk

MIX
Paper from responsible sources
FSC™ C104740

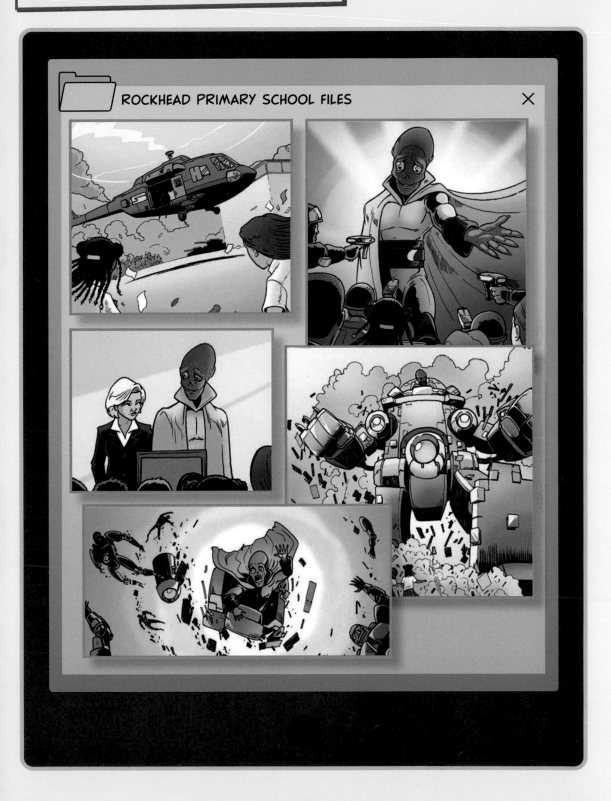

ROCKHEAD PRIMARY SCHOOL FILES

TO: SENTINELS HQ
AGENTS: RIPLEY AND ARNIE
JUNIOR AGENTS: VERNA LEE AND JAMIE BALLARD
REPORTING IN FROM: ROCKHEAD PRIMARY SCHOOL

School settling down after events of last month.

The alien Murlak arrived with an offer of new technology to help the world.

This was a trick - and turned out to be the beginning of an attack.

The attack was defeated by using the energy in the portals against the aliens, and Murlak was sent back.

School building badly damaged during the attack, repairs in progress.

Science team led by Junior Agent Verna Lee checking the alien portals.

We understand Director Keller has been fired, along with Torres from the science team.

Rockhead security team in place as ever …

Today's special assembly is all about my new five-year plan for our school ...

NEW FIVE-YEAR PLAN

This will replace my earlier plans, which were disrupted because of the ... er ... events that have taken place. The aliens haven't returned, thank goodness, so we can get back on track ...

You know what this means, don't you, Mrs Lamont. More work for us teachers.

RRRRRUUUUUUMMMMMMMBBBBBBLLLLLE ...

It almost makes me wish another 'event' might happen. Just kidding, obviously.

Ha ha! Be careful what you wish for! Hang on ... what's that strange noise?

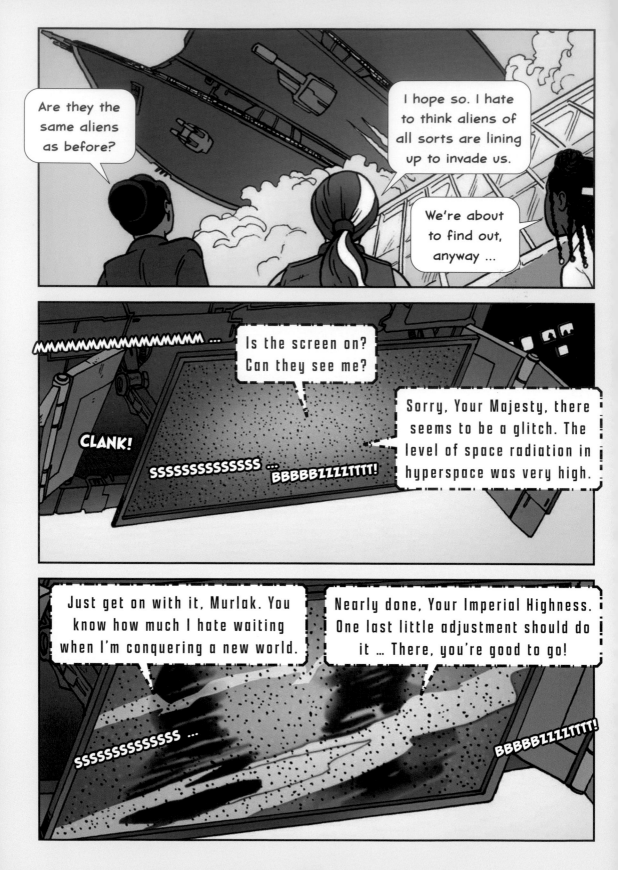

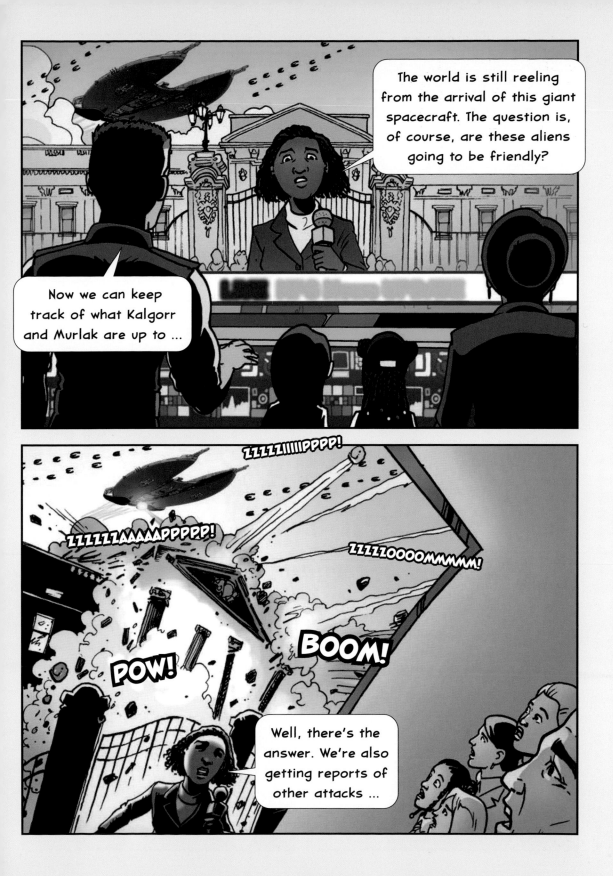

Fighter jets from all over the world are going into action against the alien invasion. But nothing seems able to stop the deadly alien drones ...

You're right, Mrs Sharma. Everyone in the world will have to work together.

It looks like this might be quite a difficult problem. These aliens do seem rather determined to conquer us.

Actually, I think ...

Could I just say ...

I don't think it will be difficult at all. We should hit them with everything we've got.

QUIET!

I know how to defeat Kalgorr.

There's no need to be rude, Verna. I'm sure you've got lots to say, as usual, but we've got this under control.

Really? I don't think so. You should listen to her. She's a genius.

Jamie is right, Mrs Sharma. Sorry, Verna ... we're listening now.

It will be easier if I show you. I'll just open the file ... Could you put it on the big screen for me, Jamie?

No problem, Verna. There you go ...

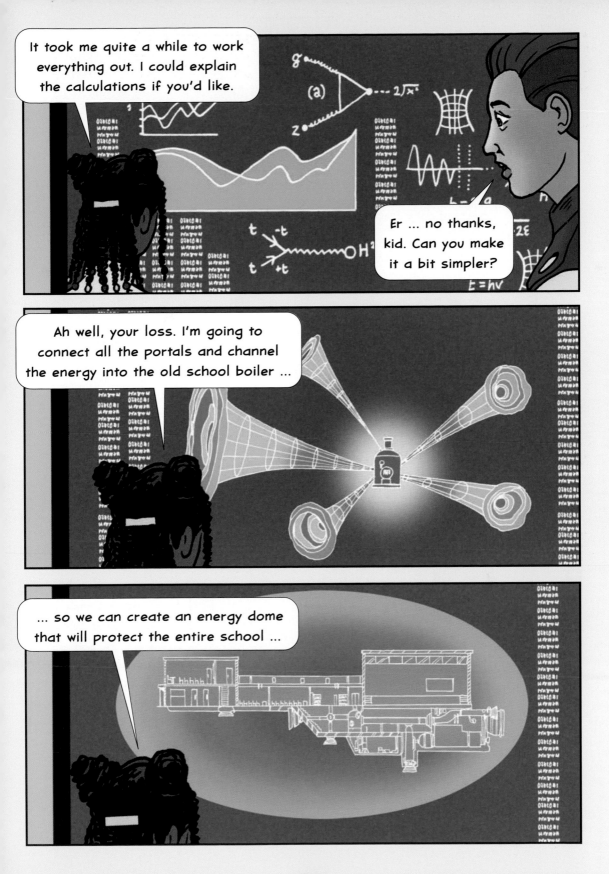

23

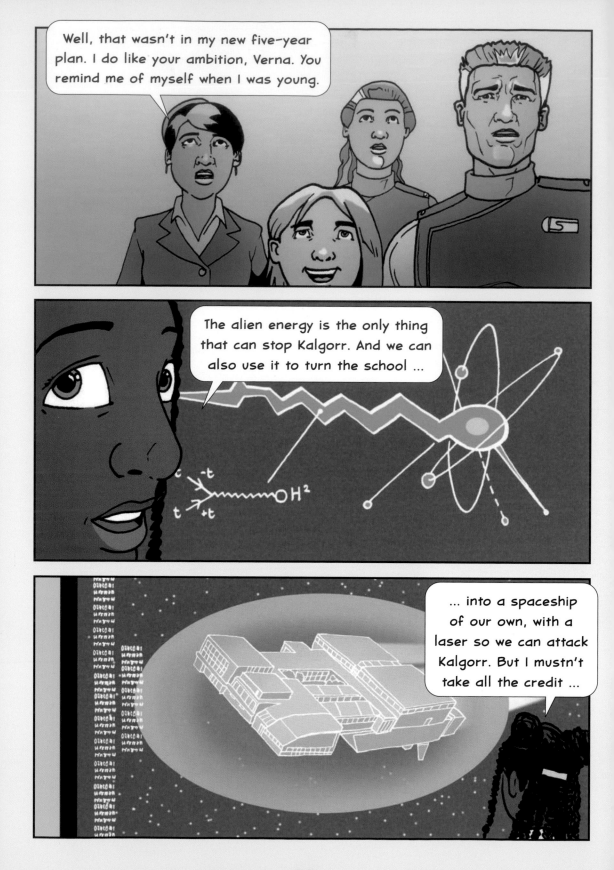

ZZZZZZAAAAAAAPPPPP!

POWWWW!

BLAM BLAM BLAMMMM!

... the laser was Jamie's idea.

That's all brilliant, Verna. In fact, I'm very impressed with both of you.

So what are we waiting for? You two better tell us what we need to do.

TRANSFORMATION PLAN

BOILER TEAM – HOPPER to lead

BRIDGE TEAM to adapt CONTROL CENTRE

MR RECKITT to secure all internal walls

MIDDAY SUPERVISORS and KITCHEN STAFF to provide meals

CHILDREN and TEACHERS to assist wherever possible

YEAR 3 to be kept occupied

Don't worry ... we've got a plan ...

29

Bother. It looks like we've run out of time after all. Any news on the dome, Verna?

Just checking ...

Bridge to Hopper. When will we have enough power for the dome?

I don't know, Verna, I've hit a few snags. Maybe half an hour?

Sorry, Hopper. I can give you a couple of minutes, but that's all.

I think Kalgorr wants to talk to us.

That's good. I've got a few things I want to say to him. Put him on the screen, Verna.

Could you keep him talking? The more time we can give Hopper, the better.

Greetings, Earthlings. I have come to accept your surrender.

Not so fast, Mr Kalgorr. You said you'd give us three hours to think about it, and you're eleven minutes and 31 seconds early.

I am the Emperor of the Veem, and if I decide to come back early, then it's hard luck. Are you going to surrender to me or not?

Hang on a minute, will you? It's really not fair to expect us to make a decision like that so quickly.

Don't listen to her, Your Majesty! We should destroy them all now ... I don't think it's a very nice planet anyway.

Really? I rather like it ...

Come on, Verna, what's happening? I can't keep him talking much longer.

Hopper, what exactly are you doing out there? Your two minutes are up!

Sorry, Verna! I've only got half power and I'm not sure that's enough ...

37

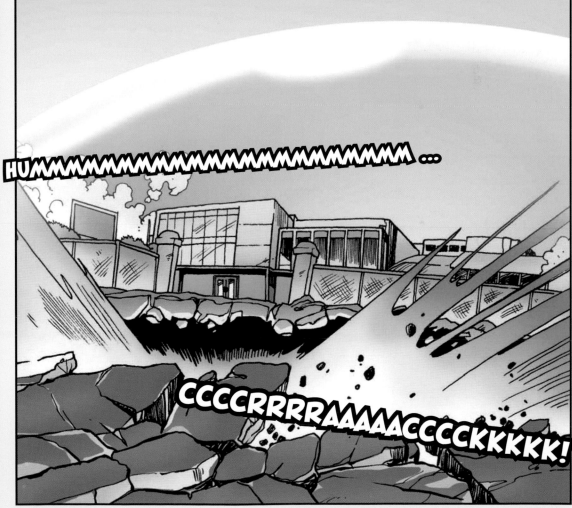

... once we've worked out what to do. Right, team. Obviously we can't stay up here in space forever – we need a plan.

I'm not sure we have a lot of options, Mrs Sharma. I could try contacting Sentinels HQ again and ask them if they've come up with anything new.

I doubt it. You saw what those drones did to our fighters. There's nothing on Earth that can stop them. If only we had our own fleet of drones like them ...

Actually, that might be possible.

I don't think so, Jamie. You can't make a load of drones in a craft lesson.

No, of course not. But we can steal them from Kalgorr and use them against him ...

Kalgorr and Murlak must control the drones from their spaceship. If we can get into their main computer we could take over the drones ourselves.

Great idea, kid. But how do you do it? Are you talking about hacking into their computer from here?

It would be easier if I could get on their spaceship. Then I could download the codes directly.

We could send in a boarding party ... Although they'd see us coming, so that isn't going to work.

I might be able to help with that. I'm certain I now know how to make ...

49

51

Ah, Mrs Jones, could you tell all the teachers we're going to have a staff meeting? I need to speak to them ...

VWWWWWHHHHOOOOSSSSSHHHHH ...

... So as you can see, we do have a plan to deal with the aliens. Over to you, Jamie.

Thanks, Mrs Sharma. It looks like the codes we downloaded will only give me control of some drones, not all of them. That means I'll have to fight the rest.

It will be like playing a computer game, and I'm good at those. But the battle won't be easy. There's only one of me, and Kalgorr has a lot of drones.

56

Good, I'm glad to see you've finally come to your senses. I told you they would surrender in the end, Murlak.

I'm sorry, I should have made it clearer. We're not surrendering to you. You're going to surrender to us.

I don't think so. You've got that completely the wrong way round!

Are you sure you don't want to think again? This is your last chance.

Of course I'm sure! This is ridiculous and you're making me very angry ...

Suit yourself. This conversation is over. Turn him off, Verna.

No problem, Mrs Sharma. Switching screen to tactical display now ...

58

64

EPILOGUE

A few days later at Rockhead Primary ...

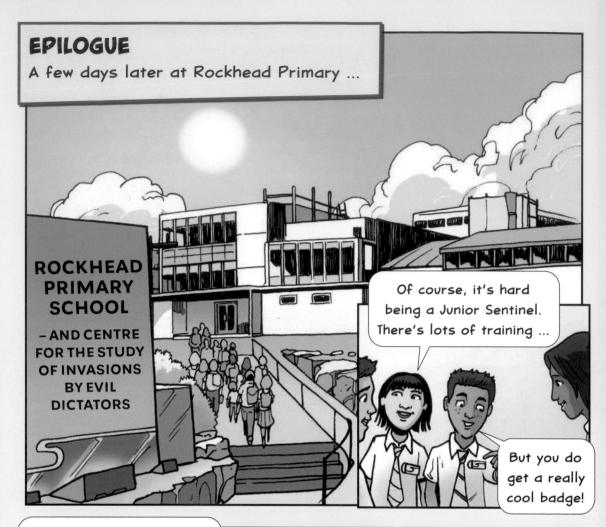

ROCKHEAD PRIMARY SCHOOL

– AND CENTRE FOR THE STUDY OF INVASIONS BY EVIL DICTATORS

Of course, it's hard being a Junior Sentinel. There's lots of training ...

But you do get a really cool badge!

I'm sorry, Mrs Sharma can't take your call. You could always try calling later, Madame President ...

It's very good of you to increase our budget, Prime Minister, I'll send you my new five-year plan ...

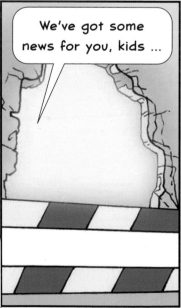

We've got some news for you, kids ...

CHAT ABOUT THE BOOK

1 What interrupted assembly at the beginning of the story?

2 Look at Page 19. What does 'reeling' mean? What other word could be used instead?

3 Read page 70. Why do you think the Prime Minister increased the budget for Rockhead Primary School?

4 Read from page 14 to the end of page 17. What do we learn about Kalgorr when he first arrives at Rockhead Primary School?

5 Look at the illustrations on page 26 and 27. How do these add to the story the author is telling?

6 On page 20, Verna says, 'QUIET!' What effect has the author created by writing it this way?

7 How does the conversation between Mrs Sharma and Kalgorr on page 57 show us what is similar about the two characters?

8 Were there any parts of the story that you found funny? Which parts were these and why do you think the author included them in the story?